Published 2015 by Geddes & Grosset, an imprint of The Gresham
Publishing Company Ltd, Academy Park, Building 4000,
Gower Street, Glasgow, G51 1PR, Scotland

Written by Judy Hamilton.
Artwork by Mimi Everett, courtesy of Simon Girling & Associates,
Hadleigh, Suffolk.

ISBN 978-1-910680-54-4

Printed and bound in Malaysia

3 4 5 6 7 8 9 10

Susie & Sam

Learn
to
Swim

G g+

Geddes & Grosset

"Mum!" called Sam. "I can't find my swimming trunks!"

"I've got them," called Mum. "Now hurry up and get your shoes on please – we have to be there in ten minutes."

Susie and Sam were going for their first swimming lesson. They had been to the swimming pool lots of times before with Mum and Dad, but they both had to wear armbands to help them to float. Now they were going to learn to swim all by themselves.

"I'm going to swim all the way across the pool by myself!" said Sam.

"One step at a time," said Dad. "It will take quite a few lessons before you can swim that far all by yourself!"

At the pool, Susie and Sam changed into their swimming costumes and Mum took them to meet Julie, their teacher.

"Come and join the others," said Julie. "Your Mum and Dad can watch from the spectators' gallery."

The other children had armbands on, just like Susie and Sam.

"When can we take our armbands off?" said Sam to Julie.

"When I say so," said Julie. "I have to see how you are getting on first."

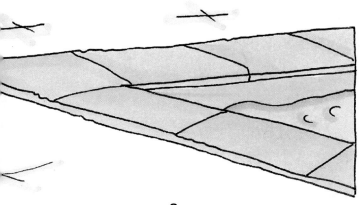

The children got into the water at the shallow end of the swimming pool. Some jumped in with a splash. Others slid into the water, very slowly.

"Now," said Julie, "jump up and down and get your hair wet."

All the children jumped up and down, but not all of them got their hair wet.

"Duck right down and put your faces under the water," said Julie.

Susie and Sam ducked down until the water went over their heads and then bobbed back up again. But the girl next to Susie kept her head out of the water.

"I don't want to do it," she said to Susie.

"Screw your eyes up tight," Susie said, "and take a deep breath. Then it's easy."

The girl screwed her eyes up tight, took a deep breath, and tried again. She ducked her head right under the water and came up again, smiling.

"Well done everybody," said Julie. "Now, let's do some kicking practice."

Julie got into the water beside the children to show them how to kick properly. Then she gave everybody a float to hold and they set off across the pool, to practise. It was hard work!

"Kick as hard as you can!" said Julie. "Swim to the rope in the middle of the pool and then back to the side!"

15

Sam kicked and splashed and kicked and splashed but hardly moved at all.

"Wait for me!" he called to Susie.

"Remember what I showed you," said Julie. "Kick properly, Sam!"

Sam tried again and this time he kicked properly. Soon he caught up with Susie.

After they had practised some more, Susie and Sam were kicking very well.

Next, Julie showed them how to move their arms.

"Stretch your arm right in front of you and keep your fingers together," she said.

"Pull down through the water, back to your side."

First they practised standing up in the water. Then they practised swimming with one arm only, holding onto a float with their other hand. Then, Julie took the floats away and asked the children to swim with both arms.

"Can we take our armbands off yet?" asked Sam.

"Not yet," said Julie. "Once you can use your legs and arms together properly, then you can try swimming without armbands."

Swimming without the float was difficult but Susie and Sam tried their best.

At last, they reached the rope, but they had to stop for breath before they swam back to the side of the pool.

"Well done," said Julie. "You have worked very hard. That's all for today."

Susie and Sam were really quite glad. It had been fun, but they were tired now.

"Well done," said Mum and Dad. "We are very proud of you."

"I still need my armbands," said Sam.

"Remember, Sam," said Dad. "One step at a time. Each lesson, you will get a little better. You'll be able to swim by yourself soon enough."

Dad was right. Every Saturday, Susie and Sam got a little better. After two more lessons, Julie let them take their armbands off and they managed to swim a few strokes without them. The next lesson, they could swim a little further.

But the best lesson was when both Susie and Sam swam all the way across the pool without their armbands. Julie gave them a certificate to put on their bedroom walls. How proud they were!

"Soon," said Susie, "we'll be able to swim for miles!"

"One step at a time!" said Sam.